English

The 11+
10-Minute Tests

For GL & other test providers

Ages
9-10

Practise • Prepare • Pass
Everything your child needs for 11+ success

How to use this book

This book is made up of 10-minute tests and puzzle pages.
There are answers and detailed explanations in the pull-out section at the back of the book.

10-Minute Tests

* There are 33 tests in this book, consisting of 17 comprehension texts worth 9 marks each, and 16 proofreading tests worth 18 marks each. Each test is a bite-sized version of a full length 11+ test, focusing on either the comprehension part or the proofreading part of the test.

* Each test is designed to cover a good range of the question styles and topics that your child could come across in their 11+ test.

* Your child should aim to score at least 8 out of 9 in each comprehension test and 16 out of 18 in each proofreading test. If they score less than this, use their results to work out the areas they need more practice on.

* If your child hasn't managed to finish the test in time, they need to work on increasing their speed, whereas if they have made a lot of mistakes, they need to work more carefully.

* Keep track of your child's scores using the progress chart on the inside back cover of the book.

Puzzle Pages

* There are 10 puzzle pages in this book. The puzzles are a great break from test preparation. They encourage children to practise the same skills that they will need in the test, but in a fun way.

Published by CGP

Editors:
Marc Barnard, Sophie Herring, Holly Robinson and Sean Walsh

With thanks to Alison Griffin and Karen Wells for the proofreading.
With thanks to Emily Smith for the copyright research.

"L. M. Montgomery" is a trademark of Heirs of L. M. Montgomery Inc.

ISBN: 978 1 78294 818 6
Printed by Elanders Ltd, Newcastle upon Tyne
Clipart from Corel®

Based on the classic CGP style created by Richard Parsons.

Contents

Test 1 2

Test 2 5

Test 3 7

Puzzles 1 .... **10**

Test 4 11

Test 5 13

Test 6 16

Puzzles 2 .... **19**

Test 7 20

Test 8 22

Test 9 25

Puzzles 3 .... **27**

Test 10 28

Test 11 30

Test 12 33

Puzzles 4 .... **35**

Test 13 36

Test 14 39

Test 15 41

Puzzles 5 .... **44**

Test 16 45

Test 17 47

Test 18 50

Puzzles 6 .... **52**

Test 19 53

Test 20 56

Test 21 59

Puzzles 7 .... **61**

Test 22 62

Test 23 64

Test 24 67

Puzzles 8 .... **69**

Test 25 70

Test 26 73

Test 27 75

Puzzles 9 .... **78**

Test 28 79

Test 29 81

Test 30 83

Puzzles 10 .... **86**

Test 31 87

Test 32 89

Test 33 92

You have **10 minutes** to do this test. Work as quickly and accurately as you can.

Read this passage carefully and answer the questions that follow.

An adapted extract from 'The Happy Prince'

High above the city, on a tall column, stood the statue of the Happy Prince. He was gilded with thin leaves of gold, for eyes he had two bright sapphires, and a large red ruby glowed on his sword-hilt. Tears were running down his golden cheeks.

A swallow alighted between his feet. "Why are you weeping?" asked the bird.

5 "When I was alive and had a human heart," answered the statue, "I did not know what tears were, for I lived in the Palace of Sans-Souci, where sorrow is not allowed to enter. Round the garden ran a lofty wall, but I never cared to ask what lay beyond it, everything about me was so beautiful. My courtiers called me the Happy Prince, and happy indeed I was, if pleasure be happiness. So I lived, and so I died. And

10 now that I am dead they have set me up here so high that I can see all the ugliness and the misery of my city, and though my heart is made of lead yet I cannot choose but weep.

"See that seamstress in a poor house. Her face is thin and worn, and she has coarse, red hands, all pricked by the needle. She is embroidering passion-flowers on

15 a satin gown for the loveliest of the Queen's maids-of-honour. In the corner of the room her little boy is lying ill with fever. Little swallow, will you not bring her the ruby out of my sword-hilt? My feet are fastened to this pedestal and I cannot move."

"I am waited for in Egypt," said the swallow. "My friends are flying up and down the Nile and they sleep in the tomb of the great King in his painted coffin." But the

20 Happy Prince looked so sad that the little swallow was sorry. "It is very cold here," he said, "but I will stay with you for one night, and be your messenger."

Oscar Wilde

Answer the following questions about the text. You can refer back to the text if you need to.

1. According to the text, which of these statements must be true?
   Tick the box next to the correct answer.

   A   The statue is outside the city walls.   ☐

   B   The statue is plated with gold.   ☐

   C   The statue is angry with the swallow.   ☐

   D   The statue is upset because of the swallow.   ☐

2. Give another word or phrase that means the same as
   "sorrow" (line 6) as it is used in the text.

   _____

3. "Round the garden ran a lofty wall, but I never cared to ask what lay beyond it,
   everything about me was so beautiful." (lines 7-8). What does this suggest about
   the prince's character? Tick the box next to the correct answer.

   A   He looked down on people who didn't live in the palace.   ☐

   B   He was afraid of the outside world.   ☐

   C   He only cared about his own life.   ☐

   D   He wanted other people to be miserable.   ☐

4. What type of word is "misery" (line 11)? Tick the box next to the correct answer.

   A   Collective noun   ☐

   B   Abstract noun   ☐

   C   Proper noun   ☐

   D   Pronoun   ☐

TURN OVER ➡

3

5. "and though my heart is made of lead yet I cannot choose but weep" (lines 11-12).
    Explain what this means in your own words.

    _____

    _____

6. Write down a word or phrase from the text that means "rough".

    _____

7. Why do you think the statue wants to give the seamstress the ruby
    from his sword-hilt?

    _____

    _____

8. Why is the swallow going to Egypt?

    _____

9. What makes the swallow change his mind? Tick the box next to the correct answer.

    A   It is very cold.   ☐

    B   He feels sorry for the seamstress.   ☐

    C   He feels sorry for the statue.   ☐

    D   He wants the ruby for himself.   ☐

END OF TEST

/ 9

You have **10 minutes** to do this test. Work as quickly and accurately as you can.

> This passage contains some spelling mistakes.
> Write the passage out again with the correct spellings.

1. Surely Lorna can't be iritated with me for to long. It had been an honist
    misstake and I have apolagised repeatedly. She will forgive me eventually.

    _____

    _____

    _____

> This passage has some punctuation mistakes.
> Write the passage out again with the correct punctuation.

2. Certain types of trees, such as oak, and beech, lose their leaves in the
    autumn (these are known as deciduous trees. Pine and holly are
    examples of evergreen trees, which means, they dont lose their leaves

    _____

    _____

    _____

    _____

TURN OVER

For each numbered line, choose the word, or group of words, which completes the passage correctly. The passage needs to make sense and be written in correct English. Circle the correct letter.

3. Animal fostering is when pets that **have** **having** **haven't** **had** **are** yet
                A   B   C   D   E

4. been adopted are placed in a temporary home **because** **rather** **instead** **that** **so**
                           A   B   C   D   E

5. than in a shelter. Some animals aren't **using** **use** **used** **uses** **being used** to
                   A   B   C   D   E

6. living with people and sometimes **it** **they** **their** **them** **they're** need specialist
                       A   B   C   D   E

7. care. A foster home **is able** **has** **which** **that** **can** give them the attention they
                A   B   C   D   E

8. need, **what** **even** **which** **also** **since** can help the animals get used to a normal
            A   B   C   D   E

9. lifestyle. **During** **If** **Being** **When** **While** fostered in this way can improve a
               A   B   C   D   E

10. pet's chances of being **adopted** **adopt** **adopting** **adopts** **adopter** permanently.
                   A   B   C   D   E

END OF TEST

/ 18

Test 3: Comprehension

You have **10 minutes** to do this test. Work as quickly and accurately as you can.

> Read this passage carefully and answer the questions that follow.

Millicent Garrett Fawcett

Women in the UK were unable to vote at the start of the 20th century. However, in 1928, a historic law was passed that gave women in the UK over the age of 21 the right to vote. Ten years earlier, the vote had been granted to a limited number of women — for example, those aged over 30 who owned property (this also included
5 land) or were married to a property owner — but the 1928 law meant that men and women could vote on equal terms. This was the culmination of years of tireless efforts by determined campaigners and a huge step forward for gender equality.

One of the most influential campaigners was Millicent Garrett Fawcett. She became an activist aged 22 and spent the rest of her life fighting for women's rights.
10 She led the National Union of Women's Suffrage* Societies (NUWSS), working with politicians who wanted to help their cause, as well as holding peaceful marches and demonstrations. Unlike the suffragettes (another movement that campaigned for women's suffrage), who famously used violent tactics to raise the profile of women's issues, Fawcett and the NUWSS firmly believed that this wasn't the answer. Although
15 she did not agree with their methods, Fawcett admired the suffragettes' courage and knew that they all believed in the same important cause.

In addition to her campaign for the vote, Fawcett was passionate about women's education and even founded an all-female college at Cambridge University. She wrote books and essays on social and political issues, including some with her
20 husband, Henry Fawcett, with whom she had one daughter. Millicent Fawcett died in 1929, one year after the goal of women's suffrage was achieved.

In 2017, it was announced that Fawcett would be the first woman to be honoured with a statue in Parliament Square in London, standing alongside figures such as Winston Churchill and Nelson Mandela.

* suffrage — *the right to vote*

TURN OVER ➡

1. In which year were women older than 30 given the right to vote?

    _____

2. Which of these words is closest in meaning to "culmination" (line 6)?
    Tick the box next to the correct answer.

    A   Reward   ☐

    B   Climax   ☐

    C   Achievement   ☐

    D   Decision   ☐

3. Explain why the 1928 law was a "huge step forward for gender equality" (line 7).

    _____

4. Which of the following describes the approach taken by Fawcett and the NUWSS?
    Tick the box next to the correct answer.

    A   They used violent methods.   ☐

    B   They fought against the suffragettes and their cause.   ☐

    C   They worked with influential people who supported their cause. ☐

    D   They refused to work with men.   ☐

5. "as well as holding peaceful marches and demonstrations" (lines 11-12). Which of these words is a verb? Tick the box next to the correct answer.

   A   holding   ☐

   B   peaceful   ☐

   C   marches   ☐

   D   demonstrations   ☐

6. The suffragettes "famously used violent tactics to raise the profile of women's issues" (lines 13-14). Explain what this means in your own words.

   _____

   _____

7. What type of word is "passionate" (line 17)?

   _____

8. According to the text, which of these statements about Fawcett must be true? Tick the box next to the correct answer.

   A   She attended Cambridge University.   ☐

   B   She wrote a book about politics with her daughter.   ☐

   C   She wanted to improve higher education for women.   ☐

   D   She met her husband after reading some of his essays.   ☐

9. Why is the statue of Fawcett particularly significant?

   _____

END OF TEST

/ 9

Puzzles 1

Time for something different. Test your **spelling** and **synonym** skills with these puzzles.

Mixed Messages

Minnie has received a letter from her friend Molly, but Molly's muddled up some homophones. Underline the words that are spelt incorrectly, then write the correct words on the lines below.

Dear Minnie,

It was grate seeing you last week!
You were an excellent guessed and
your welcome to stay again any time.
I've mist you a lot so it was brilliant
to catch up.

You need to visit again soon as I have
someone knew for you to meat — I've
adopted a little kitten called Pepper.
She's very adorable, accept she does
bite me quite a lot so we'll have to sea
weather she grows out of that.

Hope to here from you soon!
From Molly

1. _____
2. _____
3. _____
4. _____
5. _____
6. _____
7. _____
8. _____
9. _____
10. _____

Splendid Synonyms

Unscramble the anagrams below to find three synonyms. Then, write down another word that means the same as those three. The first letter has been given to help you.

M I Z N A G A   R U P E S   C I R R E T I F

_____   _____   _____

These words all mean the same as: <u>W</u> __ __ __ __ __ __ __ __

Test 4: Proofreading

You have **10 minutes** to do this test. Work as quickly and accurately as you can.

For each numbered line, choose the word, or group of words, which completes the passage correctly. The passage needs to make sense and be written in correct English. Circle the correct letter.

1. When he was younger, Martin **is** **was** **has been** **have been** **were** a fussy
                                             A   B   C   D   E

2. eater. He refused to eat vegetables **although** **therefore** **until** **which** **because**
                                              A   B   C   D   E

3. he thought **there** **they're** **their** **those** **these** smell was horrible. However,
                 A   B   C   D   E

4. now that he is older, he **would have** **would be** **will** **would** **wouldn't have**
                                 A   B   C   D   E

    happy to eat Brussels sprouts all day.

This passage contains some spelling mistakes.
Write the passage out again with the correct spellings.

5. The snow desended durring the night, settleing over the garden like a blancket. Whiskers the cat sniffed it curiosly, jabbed at it with his paw and intsantly leapt away with a hiss.

_____

_____

_____

TURN OVER ➡

This passage contains some punctuation mistakes. Each numbered line has either one mistake or no mistake. For each line, work out which group of words contains a mistake, and circle the correct letter. Circle N if there is no mistake.

6. Cathy was determined to beat Daniels team to the top of the hill. The winners

        A   B   C   D   N

7. would receive chocolates, marshmallows, and eternal glory. But it was a long

        A   B   C   D   N

8. hike and they had been walking for hours. the sky was starting to grow dark.

        A   B   C   D   N

9. Cathy's shoes were soaked through and she could feel blisters on her feet It had

        A   B   C   D   N

10. rained twice already, hayley had fallen over and they were all beyond exhausted

        A   B   C   D   N

11. after running away from a herd of cow's. Even so, Cathy refused to let herself (or

        A   B   C   D   N

12. her team) give up. She looked over her shoulder and saw four determined faces.

        A   B   C   D   N

13. "Not far now" she shouted encouragingly. "We can do this! The prize is ours!"

        A   B   C   D   N

END OF TEST

/ 18

You have **10 minutes** to do this test. Work as quickly and accurately as you can.

> Read this poem carefully and answer the questions that follow.

The Man and the Lion

A man and a lion once had a dispute,
Which was reckon'd the greatest, the man or the brute;
The lion discoursed on his side at some length,
And greatly enlarged on his courage and strength.

5   The man, one would think, had enough to reply
On his side the question, which none could deny;
But like many others who make a pretence,
He talked perfect nonsense, and thought it good sense.

   "So," says he, "don't be prating*, — look yonder, I pray,
10 At that sculpture of marble, now what will you say?
The lion is vanquished*; but as for the man
He is striding upon him; deny it who can."

   "But pray," said the lion, "who sculptured that stone?"
"One of us," said the man, "I must candidly* own."
15 "But when we are sculptors," the other replied,
"You will then on the man see the lion astride."

Marmaduke Park

* prating — *babbling*
* vanquished — *defeated*
* candidly — *truthfully*

TURN OVER ➡

         13   Test 5

Answer these questions about the text. You can refer back to the text if you need to.

1. Why were the man and the lion arguing?

   _____

2. Which of these statements is false? Tick the box next to the correct answer.

   A   The lion spoke for a long time.   ☐

   B   The lion boasted about his abilities.   ☐

   C   The lion thinks he is brave and strong.   ☐

   D   The lion lay down while he spoke.   ☐

3. Which of the words below is closest in meaning to "pretence" (line 7)?
   Tick the box next to the correct answer.

   A   Deception   ☐

   B   Confusion   ☐

   C   Mistake   ☐

   D   Embarrassment   ☐

4. "He talked perfect nonsense, and thought it good sense." (line 8).
   Explain what this line means in your own words.

   _____

   _____

5. Which of the following words best describes the man?
    Tick the box next to the correct answer.

    A   Honest   ☐

    B   Cautious   ☐

    C   Arrogant   ☐

    D   Gracious   ☐

6. Explain why the man points to the sculpture to support his argument.

    _____

    _____

7. "'One of us,' said the man" (line 14). Which of these words is a pronoun?

    _____

8. What does the lion say about the sculpture in lines 15-16?
    Tick the box next to the correct answer.

    A   If a lion had made the statue, it would look different.   ☐

    B   The sculpture is ugly.   ☐

    C   If lions made sculptures, they would be better at it than humans.   ☐

    D   The man should make a new sculpture.   ☐

9. Give a word or phrase that means the same as
    "astride" (line 16) as it is used in the text.

    _____

    END OF TEST

    / 9

You have **10 minutes** to do this test. Work as quickly and accurately as you can.

Read this passage carefully and answer the questions that follow.

York's Chocolate History

The city of York has numerous claims to fame: it's the historical capital of northern England, one of the most haunted cities in Europe and the birthplace of Guy Fawkes. However, one of York's more delicious achievements is its history of chocolate-making — confectionery giants such as Rowntree's® and Terry's
5   were founded within the city's walls.

In the 19th century, when other parts of northern England were building their economies on the textile and steel industries, York took a sweeter route. Entrepreneurs such as the Rowntree family developed successful businesses manufacturing chocolate. One of their earliest products was a drink made from
10 cocoa. The Rowntrees were Quakers* who believed in a teetotal* lifestyle and wanted to present their drinking chocolate as an alternative to alcohol. Later, they also became known for their Fruit Pastilles, which were an immediate success and led to rapid expansion of the business.

Encouraged by their Quaker beliefs, the Rowntrees wanted their success to benefit
15 the city. Joseph Rowntree — under whom the business flourished — had a strong sense of social responsibility and used his wealth to tackle poverty. He set up a number of charitable trusts and built good-quality housing for the employees at his factory. Chocolate was such an integral part of the city that, during the First World War, the Lord Mayor sent tins of Rowntree's® chocolate to all of York's soldiers serving
20 during Christmas 1914 as a memento of home and in recognition of their service.

Today, museums and festivals celebrate this important aspect of the city's heritage, while large-scale factories, as well as local artisan confectioners, ensure York remains the city of chocolate. York's sweetest tradition is well and truly alive, and sometimes when you walk through the city you can actually smell chocolate in the air.

* Quakers — *a Christian group*
* teetotal — *not drinking alcohol*

1. Find an adjective in the text that means "various".

   _____

2. According to the text, which of these statements is false?
   Tick the box next to the correct answer.

   A   There are supposedly lots of ghosts in York.   ☐

   B   Rowntree's® and Terry's started their businesses in York.   ☐

   C   Rowntree's® sold Fruit Pastilles before they sold drinking chocolate.   ☐

   D   Religious beliefs influenced the Rowntree family's business.   ☐

3. "developed successful businesses manufacturing chocolate" (lines 8-9).
   What type of word is "manufacturing"?

   _____

4. According to the text, why were Fruit Pastilles significant for Rowntree's®?
   Tick the box next to the correct answer.

   A   Fruit Pastilles were their healthiest product.   ☐

   B   They stopped making chocolate and only made Fruit Pastilles.   ☐

   C   Fruit Pastilles out-sold alcohol in York.   ☐

   D   Fruit Pastilles aided the growth of the company.   ☐

TURN OVER ➡

5. "Joseph Rowntree — under whom the business flourished" (line 15).
   Explain what this means in your own words.

   _____

6. Which of the following best describes Joseph Rowntree's legacy?
   Tick the box next to the correct answer.

   A   He worked closely with the city council.   ☐

   B   He fought in the First World War.   ☐

   C   He worked to improve the quality of life for many people.   ☐

   D   He was the richest man in York.   ☐

7. Explain why the Lord Mayor of York sent chocolate tins to soldiers.

   _____

   _____

8. According to the text, what is the status of York's chocolate industry today?
   Tick the box next to the correct answer.

   A   It is more profitable than it has ever been.   ☐

   B   It remains an important part of York's cultural and economic life. ☐

   C   It has been consigned to museums and festivals.   ☐

   D   Employment opportunities are limited in the industry.   ☐

9. "you can actually smell chocolate in the air" (line 24).
   Which of these words is a preposition?

   _____

END OF TEST

/ 9

Have a go at these puzzles to test your **word type** and **spelling** skills.

Missing Mottos

Some of the words from these well-known sayings are missing. Can you find them in the wordsearch below and complete the sayings correctly?

a) Slow and _____ wins the _____.

b) There's no place like _____.

c) A picture is worth a thousand _____.

d) The early bird catches the _____.

e) _____ makes perfect.

f) Two _____ are better than one.

g) As pretty as a _____.

L	A	R	G	H	O	M	E
G	S	D	E	K	R	A	C
C	U	S	N	O	Y	T	I
T	A	T	W	N	A	B	T
J	H	E	A	D	S	R	C
E	I	A	J	X	D	O	A
L	S	D	R	O	W	K	R
F	K	Y	B	M	I	C	P
R	A	C	E	A	E	S	L
T	P	I	C	T	U	R	E

One of the missing words is a different word type from the others.

Which word is the odd one out? _____

Explain why you chose this word: _____

Backwards and Forwards

This sentence reads the same backwards as it does forwards — its letters are in the same order both ways. Can you fill in the missing letters to work out what it says?

"W _ _ _ t _ _ _ r or _ c _ _ l s _ _ ?"

Hint: This is the middle letter

You have **10 minutes** to do this test. Work as quickly and accurately as you can.

> For each numbered line, choose the word, or group of words,
> which completes the passage correctly. The passage needs to make
> sense and be written in correct English. Circle the correct letter.

1. Eva **would** **would have** **had** **will** **can** like to move house because she wants
    A   B   C   D   E

2. to live **far** **further** **closer** **closest** **farther** to school. At the moment, she has
    A   B   C   D   E

3. to **setting** **setted** **sets** **set** **is set** off really early every morning. If she doesn't,
    A   B   C   D   E

    there isn't enough time to walk to the other side of the village, catch the bus and

4. still **made** **make** **makes** **making** **would make** it in time for her first lesson.
    A   B   C   D   E

> This passage has some punctuation mistakes.
> Write the passage out again with the correct punctuation.

5. Dentists' recommend, that you brush your teeth twice a day You should also floss
    between your teeth use mouthwash, and go for regular checkup's to keep your teeth
    healthy.

    _____

    _____

    _____

This passage contains some spelling mistakes. Each numbered line has either one mistake or no mistake. For each line, work out which group of words contains a mistake, and circle the correct letter. Circle N if there is no mistake.

6. The pots needed scrubbing, the living room needed houvering and somehow

    A   B   C   D   N

7. somebody had spiled coffee down the stairs. Henry was struggling not to panic.

    A   B   C   D   N

8. His mother had phoned him only minutes before to announce a suprise visit.

    A   B   C   D   N

9. Everything needed to be perfect or he would never here the end of it. The last

    A   B   C   D   N

10. time she had come to his new house, she had praised him for keeping the

    A   B   C   D   N

11. place so neat and tidy. He was regretting that now. It meant he had a reputacion

    A   B   C   D   N

12. to maintain and therefore he needed to make things look acceptible before she

    A   B   C   D   N

13. entered. He'd be in trouble if she new how messy he was most of the time.

    A   B   C   D   N

END OF TEST

/ 18

Test 8: Comprehension

You have **10 minutes** to do this test. Work as quickly and accurately as you can.

> Read this passage carefully and answer the questions that follow.

The Stranger

The villagers stood watching the stranger climb — a dash of blue against the dark rock. The mountain greeted any climbers with hostility, even if they knew the paths well. The shepherd's boy had seen him first and quickly sounded the alarm. "Look, down there! Someone's walking up by the stream!"

5   As the man drew closer, it became clear that he was unexpectedly small and as slender as a willow branch. He was alone and unarmed. There was no gleaming sword sat by his hip or hulking axe slung over his shoulder. In fact, he seemed to have come without anything at all, not even a cloak to shield against the wind or a small satchel of meagre possessions. Yet still he approached the village — and the

10 horde of suspicious spectators gawking at him — with the confidence of someone who knows they have nothing to fear.

From her position at the edge of the jostling crowd, Roma examined the man carefully. They didn't get many visitors in those parts, but when they did it was normally for one reason. If anyone wanted to pass through that way, if they wanted

15 to discover the secret of what lay in the lands beyond, then they had to get past the village first. No one ever had. Henrik, the greatest warrior in their village, watched his new opponent with a sombre but resigned expression. He understood his duty, but that wasn't to say he enjoyed it.

Roma glanced between the two men, feeling a sudden shiver down her back. No

20 challenger had ever beaten Henrik, she knew that. But looking at the stranger, with his calm smile, determined eyes and his bony hands raised in a gesture of peace, Roma did not think that he had come for battle.

> Answer the following questions about the text. You can refer back to the text if you need to.

1. According to the text, which of these statements must be true?
   Tick the box next to the correct answer.

       A   The stranger swims in the stream. ☐

       B   The stranger is exhausted when he reaches the village. ☐

       C   The stranger is dressed in blue. ☐

       D   The stranger looks like a shepherd. ☐

2. Find an example of personification in the text.

   _____

3. Why is the stranger compared to a willow branch (lines 5-6)?
   Tick the box next to the correct answer.

       A   He is bent double in the wind. ☐

       B   He is a thin man. ☐

       C   He has a strong connection with nature. ☐

       D   He has long, flowing hair. ☐

4. Write down a word or phrase from the text that means "shining".

   _____

5. Why is it surprising that the stranger seems confident?

   _____

   _____

TURN OVER ➡

6. Give another word or phrase that means the same as
    "gawking" (line 10) as it is used in the text.

    _____

7. Why do you think Roma is in the crowd? Tick the box next to the correct answer.

    A   She wants to understand why the stranger has come to the village.   ☐

    B   She wants to help the stranger.   ☐

    C   She is afraid of the stranger.   ☐

    D   She is the greatest warrior in the village.   ☐

8. How does Henrik feel about the possibility of fighting the stranger?
    Tick the box next to the correct answer.

    A   Excited and energetic   ☐

    B   Angry and aggressive   ☐

    C   Sad but accepting   ☐

    D   Tired but determined   ☐

9. Which of the following best describes what Roma thinks might happen
    at the end of the text? Tick the box next to the correct answer.

    A   Henrik will defeat the stranger.   ☐

    B   The stranger will defeat Henrik.   ☐

    C   The stranger will leave and go back down the mountain.   ☐

    D   Something will happen that has never happened before.   ☐

END OF TEST

/ 9

You have **10 minutes** to do this test. Work as quickly and accurately as you can.

This passage contains some spelling mistakes.
Write the passage out again with the correct spellings.

1. Maggie was starting to get desparate. She had serched high and low for a present, but nothing in the intire shop was suitible. The party was tommorrow, so she would definitely have to deside on something soon.

_____

_____

_____

_____

This passage has some punctuation mistakes.
Write the passage out again with the correct punctuation.

2. dexter woke up each morning to the deafening sound of roadworks on the street outside. Not again" he groaned throwing a pillow over his head to muffle the noise.

_____

_____

_____

TURN OVER

For each numbered line, choose the word, or group of words, which completes the passage correctly. The passage needs to make sense and be written in correct English. Circle the correct letter.

3. The quokka is an animal found **from close in with near** the coast of Australia.
                                             A   B   C   D   E

4. They look like small kangaroos and are a similar size **like as of with to**
       A B C D E

5. domestic cats. Quokkas **isn't aren't weren't couldn't hadn't** currently listed
       A   B   C   D   E

6. as an endangered species, but sadly **they they're there their that** numbers are
       A   B   C   D   E

7. decreasing. Their habitat has been reduced **while because by as since** human
       A   B   C D   E

8. activity, such as the **develop developers development developed develops**
       A   B   C   D   E

9. of farmland. This **destroys destroy destroyed destroying destruction** the plants
       A   B   C   D   E

and grasses that quokkas eat, and this in turn makes them more visible to

10. predators, **what might such as which this** include snakes, dogs and foxes.
       A   B   C   D   E

END OF TEST

/ 18

Puzzles 3

Take a break from the tests with these puzzles and practise your **word type** skills.

Canine Confessions

Each of the dogs below has a secret. For each dog, match the word types on the arrow to the underlined words in one of the secrets to work out which secret belongs to which dog.

Secrets...

1. <u>I</u> hate going <u>for</u> <u>walks</u>.
2. I'm <u>scared</u> of the <u>ginger</u> <u>cat</u> next door.
3. <u>I</u> <u>lick</u> my owner's <u>face</u> when they're sleeping.
4. My <u>favourite</u> <u>place</u> to sleep is <u>behind</u> the shed.
5. I <u>steal</u> my sister's <u>food</u> when <u>she</u> isn't looking.
6. I'm <u>digging</u> <u>under</u> the fence in the <u>garden</u>.

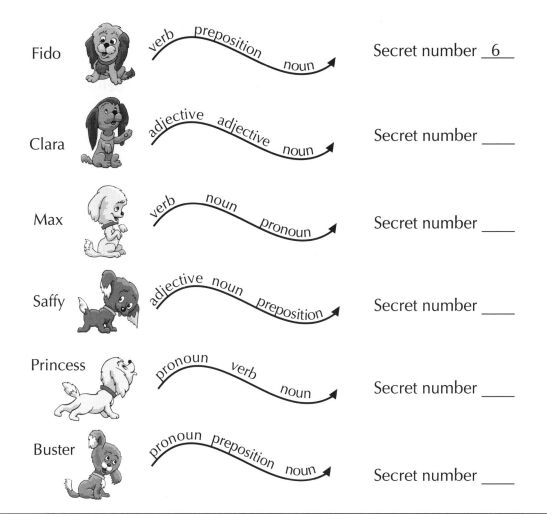

Fido — verb · preposition · noun — Secret number 6

Clara — adjective · adjective · noun — Secret number ____

Max — verb · noun · pronoun — Secret number ____

Saffy — adjective · noun · preposition — Secret number ____

Princess — pronoun · verb · noun — Secret number ____

Buster — pronoun · preposition · noun — Secret number ____

27

You have **10 minutes** to do this test. Work as quickly and accurately as you can.

> For each numbered line, choose the word which completes the passage correctly. The passage needs to make sense and be written in correct English. Circle the correct letter.

1. It **can   will   would   was   must** a lovely day for a walk. The sun was shining
      A   B   C   D   E

2. and the sky was bright blue again **once   after   because   though   from** all the
      A   B   C   D   E

3. rain last week. Buster barked excitedly as I let **his   him   he   they   them** off
      A   B   C   D   E

4. the lead and he bounded away **above   out   across   under   between** the park.
      A   B   C   D   E

> This passage contains some spelling mistakes.
> Write the passage out again with the correct spellings.

5. This recently renuvated property is sitauted in a picturesque rurul location with easy access to local shops and facilities. It boasts three spatious duble bedrooms, a cosy liveing area and a charming garden to the rear.

    _____

    _____

    _____

    _____

This passage contains some punctuation mistakes. Each numbered line has either one mistake or no mistake. For each line, work out which group of words contains a mistake, and circle the correct letter. Circle N if there is no mistake.

6. Excalibur is the | legendary sword of | king Arthur. The | blade supposedly blinded
   A | B | C | D | N

7. Arthurs enemies, while the | scabbard protected | the wearer | from mortal injury.
   A | B | C | D | N

8. There are different | account's of how | Arthur came | to possess the sword.
   A | B | C | D | N

9. According to some legends, | Arthur pulled Excalibur | from a stone | and this gave
   A | B | C | D | N

10. him the right to be king | because no-other man | had been able | to claim the sword.
    A | B | C | D | N

11. other tales say that | Excalibur was given | to Arthur | by a witch known as the
    A | B | C | D | N

12. Lady of the Lake When | Arthur died, he | ordered a knight to | throw the sword back
    A | B | C | D | N

13. into the lake. The | knight saw a hand | emerge from the | water and catch, the sword.
    A | B | C | D | N

END OF TEST

/ 18

You have **10 minutes** to do this test. Work as quickly and accurately as you can.

Read this poem carefully and answer the questions that follow.

The First Red-Bird

I heard a song at daybreak,
So honey-sweet and clear,
The essence of all joyous things
Seemed mingling in its cheer.

5   The frosty world about me
I searched with eager gaze,
But all was slumber-bound and wrapped
In violet-tinted haze.

Then suddenly a sunbeam
10 Shot slanting over the hill,
And once again from out the sky
I heard that honied trill.

And there upon a poplar*,
Poised at its topmost height,
15 I saw a little singer clad
In scarlet plumage bright.

The poplar branches quivered,
By dawn winds lightly blown,
And like a breeze-swept poppy-flower
20 The red-bird rocked and shone.

The blue sky, and his feathers
Flashed over by golden light,
Oh, all my heart with rapture thrilled,
It was so sweet a sight!

Evaleen Stein

* poplar — *a type of tree*

Answer these questions about the text. You can refer back to the text if you need to.

1.   What type of word is "joyous" (line 3)?

_____

2. Which of these statements is false? Tick the box next to the correct answer.

    A   The bird is perched at the very top of a tree. ☐

    B   The narrator has slept until late in the morning. ☐

    C   The poem takes place on a cold day. ☐

    D   The narrator thinks that the song represents happiness. ☐

3. The narrator is keen to find the source of the song.
    Which information in the poem tells you this?

    _____

4. "But all was slumber-bound and wrapped / In violet-tinted haze." (lines 7-8)
    What do these lines mean? Tick the box next to the correct answer.

    A   A bird is sleeping in its nest. ☐

    B   The garden is covered in flowers. ☐

    C   It is quiet and there is little light outside. ☐

    D   The narrator is tired. ☐

5. Find a phrase from the text that contains alliteration.

    _____

TURN OVER ➡

        31   Test 11

6. What is meant by "that honied trill" (line 12)?

_____

7. "I saw a little singer clad / In scarlet plumage bright." (lines 15-16).
   Explain what these lines mean in your own words.

_____

8. Which of the following best describes the weather in the poem?

   A   It is snowing.   ☐

   B   It is a clear day but there is a light breeze.   ☐

   C   It is wet and stormy.   ☐

   D   It is frosty and cloudy.   ☐

9. Which of the words below is closest in meaning to "rapture" (line 23)?
   Tick the box next to the correct answer.

   A   Delight   ☐

   B   Alarm   ☐

   C   Distress   ☐

   D   Emotion   ☐

END OF TEST

/ 9

You have **10 minutes** to do this test. Work as quickly and accurately as you can.

> For each numbered line, choose the word which completes the passage correctly. The passage needs to make sense and be written in correct English. Circle the correct letter.

1.   The Ancient Egyptians admired cats **for** **because** **as** **but** **since** their grace
     A   B   C   D   E

2.   and hunting ability. No one was **allow** **allowing** **allows** **allowance** **allowed**
     A   B   C   D   E

     to harm the beloved creatures and there were serious punishments for anyone who

3.   did. Even **they** **one** **some** **their** **more** of the Egyptian gods — a goddess
     A   B   C   D   E

4.   **name** **naming** **named** **calling** **calls** Bastet — was part human and part cat.
     A   B   C   D   E

> This passage has some punctuation mistakes.
> Write the passage out again with the correct punctuation.

5.   Ive only just started packing my things (even though, Dad told me to start ages ago.
     we're flying tomorrow and I still need to find my sunglasses sandals and shorts

     _____

     _____

     _____

TURN OVER ➡

This passage contains some spelling mistakes. Each numbered line has either one mistake or no mistake. For each line, work out which group of words contains a mistake, and circle the correct letter. Circle N if there is no mistake.

6. The village always orgunises a garden party at the beginning of August and I
       A   B   C   D   N

7. look forward to it every year. There's an abundance of stalls selling crafts and
       A   B   C   D   N

8. cakes, and games where you can win prizes. There are also competetions in
       A   B   C   D   N

9. various categories. Last year, I entered the baking contest and came forth, but
       A   B   C   D   N

10. hopefully I can do even better this time. The village has a great comunity spirit,
       A   B   C   D   N

11. which I adore. I used to live in the middle of a city, which definately had a
       A   B   C   D   N

12. different atmosphear. Here in the village, I see familiar faces wherever I go
       A   B   C   D   N

13. and my neighbers always stop for a chat when they notice me in the street.
       A   B   C   D   N

END OF TEST

/ 18

Time to take a break! Put your **spelling** skills to the test with these puzzles.

Spelling Bee

Using the clues in the boxes to help you, unscramble the
words below and write each word out on the line.

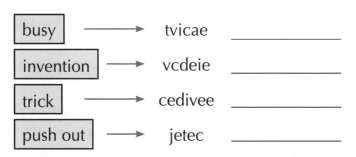

busy	→	tvicae	_____
invention	→	vcdeie	_____
trick	→	cedivee	_____
push out	→	jetec	_____

Using only the letters that appear in the four unscrambled words, what nine
letter word can you spell out? The letter 'e' has already been done for you.

__ __ __ e __ __ __ __ e   Hint: it's a word type.

Crossed Words

Each of the shapes below contains two words that have a letter in common.
Using the letters from the boxes below, can you spell out the two words?
The crossover letter has been given for you.

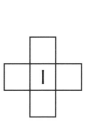

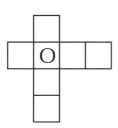

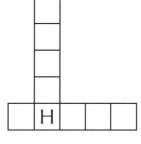

35

You have **10 minutes** to do this test. Work as quickly and accurately as you can.

> Read this passage carefully and answer the questions that follow.

An adapted extract from 'Rainbow Valley'

Jem was a sturdy, reliable little chap. He never broke a promise. He was not a great talker. His teachers did not think he was brilliant, but he was a good, all-round student. He never took things on faith; he always liked to investigate the truth of a statement for himself.

5 Once Susan had told him that if he touched his tongue to a frosty lock all the skin would tear off it. Jem had promptly done it, "just to see if it was so." He found it was "so" at the cost of a sore tongue for several days. But Jem did not grudge suffering in the interests of science. By constant experiment and observation he learned a great deal and his brothers and sisters thought his extensive knowledge of 10 their little world quite wonderful.

Jem always knew where the first and ripest berries grew, where the first pale violets shyly wakened from their winter's sleep, and how many blue eggs were in the robin's nest in the maple grove. He could tell fortunes from daisy petals and suck honey from red clovers, and dig up all sorts of edible roots on the banks of the pond, 15 while Susan went in daily fear that they would all be poisoned. He could mimic the call of any wild bird or beast and he knew the haunt of every wild flower from spring to autumn.

Jem was at present busily occupied in frying a small trout which he had just caught in the pond. His stove consisted of a circle of red stones, with a fire kindled 20 in it, and his culinary utensils were an old tin can, hammered out flat, and a fork with only one prong left.

Lucy Maud Montgomery

Answer these questions about the text. You can refer back to the text if you need to.

1. Which of these words could not be used to describe Jem?
   Tick the box next to the correct answer.

   A Dependable ☐

   B Timid ☐

   C Curious ☐

   D Quiet ☐

2. Why did Jem once touch his tongue to a frozen lock?

   _____

3. "Jem did not grudge suffering in the interests of science" (lines 7-8).
   Explain what this phrase means in your own words.

   _____

   _____

4. Which of these words is closest in meaning to "extensive" (line 9)?
   Tick the box next to the correct answer.

   A Broad ☐

   B Limited ☐

   C Average ☐

   D Uncertain ☐

TURN OVER ➡

5. "where the first pale violets shyly wakened from their winter's sleep" (lines 11-12). What is this phrase an example of? Tick the box next to the correct answer.

A   Metaphor ☐

B   Idiom ☐

C   Personification ☐

D   Simile ☐

6. What type of word is "fortunes" (line 13)?

_____

7. "while Susan went in daily fear that they would all be poisoned" (line 15). What does this tell you about Susan? Tick the box next to the correct answer.

A   She thinks Jem wants to poison them. ☐

B   She dislikes the taste of edible roots. ☐

C   She has eaten poisonous roots in the past. ☐

D   She knows less about nature than Jem does. ☐

8. Give another word or phrase that means the same as "mimic" (line 15) as it is used in the text.

_____

9. Which of the following statements is false? Tick the box next to the correct answer.

A   Jem doesn't have proper cooking equipment. ☐

B   Jem's campfire has gone out. ☐

C·   Jem is cooking with fresh ingredients. ☐

D   Jem is cooking a fish. ☐

END OF TEST

/ 9

You have **10 minutes** to do this test. Work as quickly and accurately as you can.

> This passage contains some spelling mistakes.
> Write the passage out again with the correct spellings.

1. Noah was a frequent visiter to the bookshop and he immediately notised the latest
   additon to the shelves. "Finally!" he shouted exitedly. He'd spent months waiting
   for the sequel to be relleased.

   _____

   _____

   _____

   _____

> This passage has some punctuation mistakes.
> Write the passage out again with the correct punctuation.

2. due to generous local support, our fundraiser was a huge success Were delighted
   to announce that, we exceeded our target and repair's will begin on the church roof
   next week.

   _____

   _____

   _____

TURN OVER

For each numbered line, choose the word which completes the passage correctly. The passage needs to make sense and be written in correct English. Circle the correct letter.

3. Languages need speakers **is to if when are** be considered 'alive'. When
                         A B C   D   E

4. people stop speaking a language, **they he it one who** 'dies'. This is what
                               A   B C   D   E

happened to one Native American language, Wampanoag. Until the nineteenth

5. century, it was **spoke spoked spoken speaked speak** by thousands of people,
                          A   B   C   D   E

6. but **while to from of for** a period of about 150 years it had no native speakers,
             A   B   C   D E

7. **as or but if although** English had become the main language in North America.
  A B C D   E

8. Thanks **for of with to on** the work of dedicated linguists, the language
               A B   C D E

9. has **be been being had having** reconstructed from written records, and the
          A   B   C   D   E

10. Wampanoag community have **begun begin began begin beginning** to reclaim
                                    A   B   C   D   E

this lost piece of their culture.

END OF TEST

/ 18

You have **10 minutes** to do this test. Work as quickly and accurately as you can.

Read this passage carefully and answer the questions that follow.

Mother Shipton and the Petrifying Well

The historic town of Knaresborough, North Yorkshire, is home to England's oldest visitor attraction. For hundreds of years, people have visited the incredible Petrifying Well and heard stories of the famous witch who lived nearby, Mother Shipton.

The waters of the Petrifying Well transform everyday objects into stone. This
5   phenomenon occurs because the water has a high mineral content, which causes objects left under the cascade to fossilize. In centuries past, people believed the water had strange powers — they would drink it and wash in it in order to benefit from its healing properties.

Knaresborough was also the home of Ursula Southeil, who would later become
10 known as Mother Shipton. Legend has it that she was born in a cave on the riverbank during a terrible storm. She was unpopular with the townspeople because of her ugly looks and strange ways, so she spent her time alone in the forest, learning to make potions and remedies from the plants that grew there.

Brewing potions wasn't the only string to her bow — it was said that she could
15 see the future. She became known as 'Knaresborough's Prophetess', making predictions and warning people about what was to come. She supposedly foresaw important events such as the defeat of the Spanish Armada (which took place in 1588, decades after her death in 1561) and the Great Fire of London (which occurred in 1666, over a hundred years after she died).

20 Many of these predictions were not recorded by Mother Shipton herself, but by other people in the centuries afterwards, which casts doubt over their authenticity. Nevertheless, Mother Shipton remains a celebrated figure in folklore, and tourists still visit the cave where she was born and explore the natural wonders of the forest where she lived.

TURN OVER ➡

Answer these questions about the text. You can refer back to the text if you need to.

1. What type of word is "oldest" (line 1)?

_____

2. Which of the following statements is false? Tick the box next to the correct answer.

    A   Knaresborough is the most ancient town in England.   ☐

    B   According to legend, Mother Shipton had magical powers.   ☐

    C   The Petrifying Well can turn things into stone.   ☐

    D   Knaresborough has a long history as a tourist attraction.   ☐

3. What is the reason for the Petrifying Well's unusual ability?

_____

4. How did local people feel about Ursula? Tick the box next to the correct answer.

    A   They were afraid of her because of her powers.   ☐

    B   They thought she was odd and made her an outcast.   ☐

    C   They blamed her for causing a terrible storm.   ☐

    D   She was a valued member of their community.   ☐

5. "Brewing potions wasn't the only string to her bow" (line 14).
   Explain what this phrase means in your own words.

_____

_____

6. According to the text, which of the following best describes
   Mother Shipton's prophecies? Tick the box next to the correct answer.

   A   Her potions helped her to make prophecies. ☐

   B   She made her first prediction in 1561. ☐

   C   She saw events far in the future. ☐

   D   She used palm-reading to tell people their fortunes. ☐

7. "She supposedly foresaw important events" (lines 16-17).
   Which of these words is an adverb? Tick the box next to the correct answer.

   A   She ☐

   B   supposedly ☐

   C   important ☐

   D   events ☐

8. Why do people doubt the reliability of Mother Shipton's predictions?

   _____

   _____

9. Give another word or phrase that means the same as
   "celebrated" (line 22) as it is used in the text.

   _____

END OF TEST

/ 9

Have a go at these puzzles to practise your **spelling** and **punctuation** skills.

Crossword Contrasts

Fill in the crossword by finding an antonym for each of the words below.

Across

2. lazy
4. familiar
7. empty
9. dangerous
10. protect

Down

1. damage
3. shy
5. foolish
6. friend
8. fiery

Punctuation Party

Mona is throwing a surprise party for her sister. To keep it extra secret, she has hidden the time of the party in a message.

The time is the same as the number of punctuation mistakes in the message. Identify the mistakes and work out what time the party starts.

I've booked tickets to go to london next-week (its something I've wanted to do for ages. Im going to visit the palace, look round the museums and walk by the river

The party starts at: _____ o'clock

You have **10 minutes** to do this test. Work as quickly and accurately as you can.

> For each numbered line, choose the word which completes
> the passage correctly. The passage needs to make sense
> and be written in correct English. Circle the correct letter.

1. Theo sat **quieten** **quiet** **quietly** **quiets** **quite** on the sand dunes as the
    A   B   C   D   E

2. sun began to **rises** **setting** **sets** **set** **risen**. A dull red had filled the sky and the
                  A   B   C   D   E

3. air had suddenly **becomes** **becoming** **become** **became** **becomed** crisp.
                      A   B   C   D   E

4. He zipped **up** **off** **around** **over** **in** his jacket and shivered.
               A   B   C   D   E

> This passage contains some spelling mistakes.
> Write the passage out again with the correct spellings.

5. Becky noticed the parsel under her brother's bed and was filled with curiousity. Her
    twelth birthday was next week, and she wundered whether it was a gift for her. Her
    thoughts were interupted by the familier sound of her brother's footsteps on the stairs.

    _____

    _____

    _____

    _____

TURN OVER ➡

This passage contains some punctuation mistakes. Each numbered line has either one mistake or no mistake. For each line, work out which group of words contains a mistake, and circle the correct letter. Circle N if there is no mistake.

6. This year, the school sport's day took place in the middle of a heatwave. George

    A   B   C   D   N

7. was doing the shot put. This wasn't because he had any sporting ability but

    A   B   C   D   N

8. because hed tried to wriggle his way out of doing anything. No one had wanted

    A   B   C   D   N

9. to do the shot put, so Mr Burgess, the PE teacher said George had to do it.

    A   B   C   D   N

10. As he stepped up to the mark, the heat was as stifling as his nerves. He could

    A   B   C   D   N

11. feel hundred's of eyes on him. He spun round, closed his eyes and hoped for

    A   B   C   D   N

12. the best When he reopened them, the audience were aghast. He'd broken the

    A   B   C   D   N

13. school record. "Well done," George! Mr Burgess shouted from the sidelines.

    A   B   C   D   N

END OF TEST

/ 18

Test 17: Comprehension

You have **10 minutes** to do this test. Work as quickly and accurately as you can.

Read this passage carefully and answer the questions that follow.

Midnight Mission

Edward lay down on the top bunk, closed his eyes and pretended to go to sleep.

After twenty minutes, he cautiously opened one eyelid, glancing around to make sure the other boys in his dorm were all asleep. He crept carefully down the ladder of his bunk, careful not to wake Greg, who was sleeping underneath. His heart
5 thudded against his chest.

Thud, thud, THUD.

James, who slept in the bunk next to Edward's, had come hurtling down his ladder, thumping loudly as he hit the floor. It was a miracle he didn't wake the whole dorm up.

10 "Shh!" Edward hissed at him through gritted teeth. He grabbed James by the wrist and dragged him into the corridor.

James seemed utterly incapable of speaking quietly. "What are you doing? Can I join in?" He said, grinning dumbly.

Edward found James endlessly irritating. He had all the enthusiasm of a golden
15 retriever, but with even less tact — he certainly wasn't the kind of person Edward wanted as a criminal accomplice.

But Edward was cunning, and knew how James could be valuable to him. "I'm raiding the kitchen for biscuits. You go and get them and I'll distract Mr Mulholland."

20 James went off to the kitchen and Edward waited for his cue. Not long after, the clatter of pans echoed throughout the house and the furious footsteps of Mr Mulholland stormed down the corridor. Edward used this opportunity to sneak into the housemaster's office, where the real treasure lay. He opened a drawer and pulled out his confiscated mobile phone.

TURN OVER ➡

Answer these questions about the text. You can refer back to the text if you need to.

1. Explain why Edward pretended "to go to sleep" (line 1)?

    _____

    _____

2. "He crept carefully down the ladder" (line 3).
    Which of these words is a verb? Tick the box next to the correct answer.

    A   he   ☐

    B   carefully   ☐

    C   ladder   ☐

    D   crept   ☐

3. How do you think Edward is feeling when he's climbing out of bed?
    Tick the box next to the correct answer.

    A   Nervous   ☐

    B   Confident   ☐

    C   Furious   ☐

    D   Shy   ☐

4. Write down a word or phrase from the text that means the same as 'unable'.

    _____

5. What does Edward think about James? Tick the box next to the correct answer.

   A   He's a close and loyal friend.   ☐

   B   He's annoying but can be easily manipulated.   ☐

   C   He's clever and cunning.   ☐

   D   He's nasty and unpleasant.   ☐

6. Give another word or phrase that means the same as "raiding" (line 18)
    as it is used in the text.

    _____

7. In your own words, explain what the phrase "Edward waited for his cue"
    (line 20) means.

    _____

    _____

8. Explain why Edward asks James to raid the kitchen.

    _____

    _____

9. How do you think Mr Mulholland feels at the end of the text?

    _____

END OF TEST

/ 9

49

You have **10 minutes** to do this test. Work as quickly and accurately as you can.

> For each numbered line, choose the word which completes the passage correctly. The passage needs to make sense and be written in correct English. Circle the correct letter.

1. **Wiped   Wipes   Wope   Wiping   Wipe**   the toast crumbs from his mouth, Charles
   A   **B**   **C**   **D**   **E**

2. looked at his watch. He was late! He grabbed   **their   my   her   his   your**
   A   **B**   **C**   **D**   **E**

3. school bag and ran to the bus stop.   **When   Where   Who   While   Whereas**   he
   A   **B**   **C**   **D**   **E**

4. got there, he watched   **once   than   then   as   after**   the bus went off without him.
   A   **B**   **C**   **D**   **E**

> This passage has some punctuation mistakes.
> Write the passage out again with the correct punctuation.

5. Mrs moffats bakery was very popular. Stretching all the way outside the building
   the queue was longer than ever Karen wanted to order "three blueberry muffins
   and one chocolate chip muffin."

   _____

   _____

   _____

   _____

This passage contains some spelling mistakes. Each numbered line has either one mistake or no mistake. For each line, work out which group of words contains a mistake, and circle the correct letter. Circle N if there is no mistake.

6. Maria and I found a pleasant spot and started tucking into our picnick. We'd

      A   B   C   D   N

7. packed jam sanwiches, sausage rolls and lemonade. I had just picked up a

      A   B   C   D   N

8. sausage roll when a squirrel appeared. Hesitently approaching the basket, the

      A   B   C   D   N

9. squirrel sniffed nervously. Maria tore off a small piece of bread and through

      A   B   C   D   N

10. it to the squirrel. It quickly grabbed the morsel and scuried off into the woods.

      A   B   C   D   N

11. A few minutes later, the squirrel returned with ten other companions. At that

      A   B   C   D   N

12. moment, they herled themselves onto the basket and stole our food. As we tried

      A   B   C   D   N

13. to shoo them away, the squirrels hissed and bared their teeth. We ran, terrifyed.

      A   B   C   D   N

END OF TEST

/ 18

Time for some puzzles! Take a break and practise your **vocabulary** skills at the same time.

Code Chaos

Robot Robbie has malfunctioned and can only communicate through a numbered code. Work out which letter of the alphabet each number represents and decode Robbie's message. Use the grid below to help keep track of the letters that you have decoded. Not all letters appear in the message.

```
_-_   _-_-_-R-E   _-_-R-T-_   _-_-_-E   B-E-E-_
1 13   7 4 15 6 19   4 15 6 8 7   22 15 10 19   16 19 19 2
```

```
_-T-_-_-E-_   B-_   T-_-E   E-_-_-_
7 8 3 26 19 2   16 13   8 22 19   19 10 23 26
```

22-19-26-4

```
R-_-B-_-T   R-_-G-E-R
6 3 16 3 8   6 3 21 19 6
```

A	B	C	D	E	F	G	H	I	J	K	L	M
		16		19		21						

N	O	P	Q	R	S	T	U	V	W	X	Y	Z
				6		8						

Scary Spellings

The words on the left are all synonyms of 'scary'. Fill in the missing letters to spell out the five words. Write the letters in blue in the box to the right and then rearrange them to uncover the final word.

__ r __ g __ __ e ▢ __ __ g

▢▢ r r __ __ y __ __ __

a __ a __ ▢ __ n __

__ ▢ e e __ y

▢ __ o ▢ k __

— — — — — — — —

You have **10 minutes** to do this test. Work as quickly and accurately as you can.

Read this poem carefully and answer the questions that follow.

November

I'm eleventh of twelve — perhaps not the best place
In the order of months of the year.
Rain and storm, mist and fog,
They hardly inspire folk to cheer.
5   I'm stuck at the end, dark mornings and nights,
Woefully lacking in summer's delights.

I feel quite downcast when I see the world
Without its bright green coat of leaves.
The trees are so bare, their branches like bones.
10   During my reign, a part of me grieves.
Sometimes I wish I could just change my slot,
But the rest of them say I should live with my lot.

June and July claim the sunshine and warmth.
March is all new life and flowers.
15   January's proud to be first of us all.
April has Fools' Day to make up for showers.
My neighbour December is cold, grim and grey,
Yet still is redeemed by her twenty-fifth day.

But I should remember, while tempted to sulk,
20   That plenty find joy in my weeks.
There's beauty in bleakness, artwork in autumn.
Perhaps, for a few, with me the year peaks.
"The colours!" they cry. "The orange and gold!"
This brings me a smile against the rain and the cold.

TURN OVER

1. Which of these is not a reason why November dislikes being the eleventh month?
    Tick the box next to the correct answer.

    A   The weather is miserable in November.   ☐

    B   Summer is a more cheerful time.   ☐

    C   It gets dark early in the evening in November.   ☐

    D   November wanted to be the twelfth month.   ☐

2. "Woefully lacking in summer's delights" (line 6).
    Explain what this line means in your own words.

    _____

3. What makes November feel "downcast" (line 7)?

    _____

4. Find a phrase from the text that contains a simile.

    _____

5. According to the poem, which of the following must be true?
    Tick the box next to the correct answer.

    A   Lots of animals are born in June.   ☐

    B   January is the most beautiful time of year.   ☐

    C   November would like to swap places with March.   ☐

    D   April is typically a rainy month.   ☐

6. Describe how November feels about December.

_____

_____

7. Which of these words is closest in meaning to "grim" (line 17)?
    Tick the box next to the correct answer.

    A   Bleak   ☐

    B   Difficult ☐

    C   Rough   ☐

    D   Boring   ☐

8. Why does November feel better at the end of the poem?
    Tick the box next to the correct answer.

    A   November likes the autumn colours.   ☐

    B   November thinks that for some people it is the best month.   ☐

    C   The month of November is coming to an end.   ☐

    D   The other months like November best of all.   ☐

9. "This brings me a smile" (line 24). Which of these words is a noun?

_____

END OF TEST

/ 9

Test 20: Comprehension

You have **10 minutes** to do this test. Work as quickly and accurately as you can.

Read this passage carefully and answer the questions that follow.

The Ugly Animal Preservation Society

When people think about endangered species, the same animals typically spring to mind: pandas, tigers and elephants. However, there are some endangered species (such as the blobfish, the naked mole-rat and the pig-nosed turtle) that don't usually receive the same level of support. This is something the Ugly Animal Preservation
5   Society aims to change.

Founded by biologist and comedian Simon Watt, the society raises awareness of endangered animals that are overlooked because they are deemed 'ugly'. It's no ordinary campaign though — comedians and scientists stage performances around the nation, each making the case for a different 'ugly' endangered animal.
10   Although performers make jokes at the animals' expense, they ultimately inform their audience about little-known and at-risk species. At the end of the show, the audience vote for their favourite animal and elect it as their local ugly animal mascot. For example, the mascot for London is the proboscis monkey, known for its enormous nose, while Cambridge champions endangered sea slugs.
15   In 2013, the project invited the public to help them choose an overall mascot — one to represent the society as a whole. People cast their votes from all over the world and eventually the blobfish was declared the winner. These deep sea fish are very light with little muscle, which helps them drift along the ocean floor, but when they're taken out of water their bodies sag. This gives them a lumpy shape and a
20   sorrowful expression, which has led to their label of 'ugly'. The species is at risk because they get caught up in the nets of fishing trawlers. The blobfish might not be as majestic as a snow leopard or as endearing as a red squirrel, but as the society is keen to stress, that certainly doesn't mean it deserves to be disregarded.

1. Which of the following claims does the text make about animal conservation? Tick the box next to the correct answer.

    A   The pig-nosed turtle is more endangered than the panda. ☐

    B   Certain endangered species are given more attention than others. ☐

    C   Tigers are the most endangered animals. ☐

    D   Some endangered species deserve more funding than others. ☐

2. "This is something the Ugly Animal Preservation Society aims to change" (lines 4-5). What type of word is "change" as it is used in this sentence?

    _____

3. According to the text, what is unusual about how the society raises awareness of endangered species? Tick the box next to the correct answer.

    A   They run most of their campaigns online. ☐

    B   They allow the public to interact with endangered animals. ☐

    C   They focus on teaching children about endangered animals. ☐

    D   They use humour to educate the public. ☐

4. Explain why the audience vote at the end of the show.

    _____

    _____

TURN OVER ➡

5. Which of these statements is false? Tick the box next to the correct answer.

      A   Fishing trawlers are a danger to blobfish. ☐

      B   The society has received international attention. ☐

      C   The blobfish was selected as the official face of the society. ☐

      D   Simon Watt picked the blobfish as the society's mascot. ☐

6. Which of these words is closest in meaning to "sag" (line 19)?
    Tick the box next to the correct answer.

      A   Droop ☐

      B   Crumble ☐

      C   Wobble ☐

      D   Dissolve ☐

7. How are blobfish suited to their habitat at the bottom of the ocean?

    _____

    _____

8. Write down a word or phrase from the text that means 'magnificent'.

    _____

9. "as the society is keen to stress, that certainly doesn't mean it deserves to be
    disregarded" (lines 22-23). Explain what this means in your own words.

    _____

END OF TEST

/ 9

You have **10 minutes** to do this test. Work as quickly and accurately as you can.

This passage contains some spelling mistakes.
Write the passage out again with the correct spellings.

1. The castle is the area's most populer attractian. The ancient structure's distinctive
    towers draw in thousands of visitors every year, boosting the region's econamy and
    creating a vareity of jobs in the tourist industry.

    _____

    _____

    _____

    _____

This passage has some punctuation mistakes.
Write the passage out again with the correct punctuation.

2. What have you done now" claire sighed running over to her brother. he could be
    such a little terror sometimes.

    _____

    _____

    _____

TURN OVER ➡

For each numbered line, choose the word, or group of words, which completes the passage correctly. The passage needs to make sense and be written in correct English. Circle the correct letter.

3. The Chrysler Building in New York City stands **of with in at for** 318.9 m tall.
   A   B   C   D   E

4. Financed by tycoon Walter Chrysler, it **built building builds had built was built**
       A   B   C   D   E

5. with the intention of being **a the that one this** tallest building in the world.
     A   B   C   D   E

6. At the time, a number of buildings in New York **was would had were which**
       A   B   C   D   E

7. competing for the same title, but when its construction finished **in on at with by**
       A   B   C   D   E

8. 1930, the goal was achieved. **Therefore However When Since After**, when
       A   B   C   D   E

   the Empire State Building was completed eleven months later, it was over 100 m

9. **tall tallest taller high height** than the Chrysler Building. Nevertheless,
     A   B   C   D   E

10. Chrysler's **structures structure structured structuring structural** remains one
        A   B   C   D   E

of New York City's most famous sights.

END OF TEST

/ 18

Take a break with these puzzles and practise your **word-making** skills at the same time.

Word Chain Challenge

Complete the word chain by changing one letter each time.
The underlined letters show what has changed from the previous word.

wash ⌒⌒ __wish__ ⌒⌒ wisp ⌒⌒ _____ ⌒⌒ wa_r_p ⌒⌒ war_n_

coat ⌒⌒ _____ ⌒⌒ _____ ⌒⌒ ca_s_h ⌒⌒ _____ ⌒⌒ ca_m_e

late ⌒⌒ _____ ⌒⌒ _l_ine ⌒⌒ _____ ⌒⌒ _____ ⌒⌒ face

pack ⌒⌒ _____ ⌒⌒ pe_r_k ⌒⌒ _____ ⌒⌒ pea_r_ ⌒⌒ pe_e_r

Sorting Syllables

Using syllables from the boxes below, fill in the missing words.
The numbers in brackets tell you how many syllables are in
each word. The first one has been done for you.

SPRIN	TED	NA	FI	BE	BY	O	SHEL	NEAR	PER

CHOC	GAN	TER	PA	~~COR~~	LLY	LATE	NEWS	~~NER~~

Lawrence went to the __corner__ (2) shop. He bought a _____ (3)

and a bar of _____ (3). On his way home, it suddenly _____ (2)

to snow. He took _____ (2) in a _____ (2) cafe. When it

_____ (3) stopped, he _____ (2) home as quickly as he could.

You have **10 minutes** to do this test. Work as quickly and accurately as you can.

For each numbered line, choose the word which completes
the passage correctly. The passage needs to make sense
and be written in correct English. Circle the correct letter.

1. Kris watched her **previously former older recently soon** band with glee as
               A   B   C   D   E

2. they twanged, thudded and shrieked **in over out without off** of tune.
               A   B   C   D   E

3. She **knew known know knows knowed** that she was the best guitarist in
         A   B   C   D   E

4. school and they **was is are will were** fools for kicking her out of the band.
          A   B   C   D   E

This passage contains some spelling mistakes.
Write the passage out again with the correct spellings.

5. Ella was cooking a three corse meal and she was finding it quite challenging. She
    got destracted stirring the soup and forgot about the potatos in the oven. As she
    began prepering the vegetables, smoak filled the room and the fire alarm went of.

    _____

    _____

    _____

    _____

This passage contains some punctuation mistakes. Each numbered line has either one mistake or no mistake. For each line, work out which group of words contains a mistake, and circle the correct letter. Circle N if there is no mistake.

6. While travelling around Italy in 1912, Wilfrid Voynich a Polish book dealer,

    A   **B**   **C**   **D**   **N**

7. happened upon some unusual texts. Among them, there was one tatty and

    A   **B**   **C**   **D**   **N**

8. apparently unremarkable medieval manuscript that "turned out" to be more

    A   **B**   **C**   **D**   **N**

9. interesting than it looked It was written in a completely unknown language

    A   **B**   **C**   **D**   **N**

10. and in an entirely unfamiliar, script. The text became known as the Voynich

    A   **B**   **C**   **D**   **N**

11. manuscript, and has baffled scientists and amateurs alike since it's discovery.

    A   **B**   **C**   **D**   **N**

12. Alongside the text, there are hand-drawn pictures on nearly every page. they

    A   **B**   **C**   **D**   **N**

13. seem to be scientific, but no-body has been able to work out their meaning.

    A   **B**   **C**   **D**   **N**

END OF TEST

/ 18

Test 23: Comprehension

You have **10 minutes** to do this test. Work as quickly and accurately as you can.

> Read this passage carefully and answer the questions that follow.

An adapted extract from 'The Book of Dragons'

There was once an old, old castle — it was so old that its walls and towers and turrets and gateways and arches had crumbled to ruins, and of all its old splendour there were only two little rooms left; and it was here that John the blacksmith had set up his forge. He was too poor to live in a proper house, and no one asked any rent
5 for the rooms in the ruin, because all the lords of the castle had been dead and gone for years.

John did all the work which came his way. This was not much, because most of the trade went to the mayor of the town, who was also a blacksmith. The mayor had a huge forge facing the square of the town, and had twelve apprentices, all
10 hammering like a nest of woodpeckers, and twelve journeymen* to order the apprentices about. So of course the townspeople, whenever they wanted a horse shod or a shaft mended, went to the mayor. John the blacksmith struggled on as best he could, with a few odd jobs from travellers and strangers who did not know what a superior forge the mayor's was.

15 The two rooms were warm and weather-tight, but not very large; so the blacksmith kept his old iron, his odds and ends, and his coal in the great dungeon down under the castle. It was a very fine dungeon indeed, with a handsome vaulted* roof, and at one end was a broken flight of wide steps leading down no one knew where. Even the lords of the castle in the good old times had never known
20 where those steps led to. The blacksmith had never dared to go beyond the seventh step — so he did not know what was at the bottom of those stairs.

E. Nesbit

* journeymen — *trained workers*
* vaulted — *arched*

1. Which of these words best describes the castle?
    Tick the box next to the correct answer.

    A   Disgusting   ☐

    B   Derelict   ☐

    C   Sinister   ☐

    D   Mediocre   ☐

2. Write down a word or phrase that means the same as "splendour" (line 2).

    _____

3. Why does John live in a castle? Tick the box next to the correct answer.

    A   He is a very rich man.   ☐

    B   The castle is abandoned.   ☐

    C   He is the lord of the castle.   ☐

    D   The rent for the castle is cheap.   ☐

4. According to the text, which of these statements is false?
    Tick the box next to the correct answer.

    A   John's business faces competition from the mayor.   ☐

    B   The mayor employs many people.   ☐

    C   Local residents prefer the mayor's forge.   ☐

    D   John is fussy about the work that he accepts.   ☐

TURN OVER ➡

5. Find a phrase from the text that contains a simile.

_____

6. Why do travellers go to John's forge rather than the mayor's?
Tick the box next to the correct answer.

    A   John's work is of a better quality than the mayor's. ☐

    B   John's forge is easier to get to than the mayor's. ☐

    C   John charges less for his work. ☐

    D   The travellers don't know that the mayor's forge is better. ☐

7. "The two rooms were warm and weather-tight" (line 15).
Which of these words is a noun?

_____

8. Why is the dungeon more suitable for storing John's equipment?

_____

9. Why doesn't John know what is at the bottom of the stairs?
Tick the box next to the correct answer.

    A   The steps are too broken to walk down. ☐

    B   The dungeon belongs to someone else. ☐

    C   He is afraid to go that far down. ☐

    D   The door at the bottom is locked. ☐

END OF TEST

/ 9

66

You have **10 minutes** to do this test. Work as quickly and accurately as you can.

> For each numbered line, choose the word which completes
> the passage correctly. The passage needs to make sense
> and be written in correct English. Circle the correct letter.

1. Joe stood with his back **next close over against in** the wall by the park. He
                     A   B   C   D   E

2. was **tried try trying tries trieing** not to make a noise, but he was breathing
          A   B   C   D   E

3. heavily. He peered nervously **by over round through in** the corner. The
                          A   B   C   D   E

4. three school bullies **was is are would were** there, kicking a can around.
                 A B C   D   E

> This passage has some punctuation mistakes.
> Write the passage out again with the correct punctuation.

5. "Would you like to come to the beach" with me tomorrow," Julie asked.
    "Excellent Idea!" I replied. Ill pack some sandwiches.

    _____

    _____

    _____

TURN OVER ➡

This passage contains some spelling mistakes. Each numbered line has either one mistake or no mistake. For each line, work out which group of words contains a mistake, and circle the correct letter. Circle N if there is no mistake.

6. Bernadette colapsed into the armchair, sour-faced. "I'm so bored!" She

         A   B   C   D   N

7. winged, as the opening credits for the fourth episode of 'Home Makeover

         A   B   C   D   N

8. Mayhem' in a row began. Her dad was tired of her mowning and wanted

         A   B   C   D   N

9. to watch his programmes in piece. "Why don't you go outside then?" he

       A   B   C   D   N

10. growled irritibly. "It's a beautiful day. Surely your friends will want to go out."

         A   B   C   D   N

11. "I don't want to!" Bernadette was insistent that she wouldn't budge. She

         A   B   C   D   N

12. sat sulking in silence. She was embarrassed that none of her friends wanted

         A   B   C   D   N

13. to play with her — they had fallen out with her after she had lyed to them.

         A   B   C   D   N

END OF TEST

/ 18

Time for something a bit different. Practise your **word-making** skills with these puzzles.

Cube Words

Find the answers to these clues using just the letters in the cube. You can only use each letter once in each word, and every answer must use the letter 'E'.

A	E	V
R	E	T
N	D	U

another word for 'quilt' ....

a verb meaning 'to hire' ....

another word for 'below' ....

There's a nine-letter word hidden in the grid. Can you find it?

- - - - - - - - - - -

Suffix Swap

Stephanie has finished her suffix puzzle, but she's got some wrong. Tick or cross the boxes to say whether she's found a correct match or not. If the match is wrong, write what the suffix should be on the line below. You can only correct the words using the incorrectly used suffixes from the puzzle.

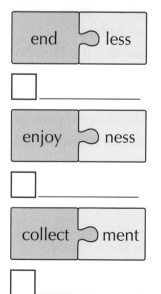

end 〕less

□ _____

enjoy 〕ness

□ _____

collect 〕ment

□ _____

aware 〕ment

□ _____

shy 〕ness

□ _____

tired 〕ity

□ _____

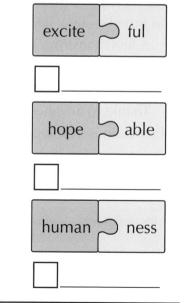

excite 〕ful

□ _____

hope 〕able

□ _____

human 〕ness

□ _____

Test 25: Comprehension

You have **10 minutes** to do this test. Work as quickly and accurately as you can.

> Read this passage carefully and answer the questions that follow.

Deep Sea Creatures

Most sea creatures that live in the ocean reside in the warm, sunlit areas near the surface. As you dive deeper, the ocean gets colder and darker with fewer and fewer plants — this is because there is no sunlight to help the plants grow. This means that deep sea creatures have to find other sources of food. They mainly rely on dead
5   animals, such as the corpses of whales, falling from near the ocean surface to the ocean floor for food.

Many of the animals that lurk in these darkened depths have evolved to look gruesome — well, who needs to look good when no one can see you? The anglerfish is one of the most well-known — and most terrifying. With rows of long,
10 fang-like teeth, and flexible jaws and bodies, they can swallow prey up to twice their own size. Anglerfish got their name from the long rod protruding from their heads with an incandescent* lure at the end, which they use to attract prey.

Another odd resident of the depths is the vampire squid. This creature gained its name from its dark colour, red eyes and webbed arms, which it can draw over itself
15 like a cloak. Unlike their fictional namesakes, however, vampire squids don't feed on blood — they eat organic debris that sinks from the ocean surface.

A less monstrous sea creature to prowl the ocean's dark abyss is the Dumbo octopus — so called because it resembles a little pink elephant with large ear-like fins.
20   Thanks to advances in technology, our understanding of the deepest parts of the ocean is developing all the time and new species are still being discovered. However, there is still so much to be learnt about this remote and mysterious environment.

* incandescent — *glowing*

1. According to the text, why do most sea creatures live near the surface?
    Tick the box next to the correct answer.

    A   There are fewer predators.   ☐

    B   The pressure is lower.   ☐

    C   There is more oxygen.   ☐

    D   There are more plants for them to eat.   ☐

2. Write down a word or phrase from the text that means 'hideous'.

    _____

3. "lurk in these darkened depths" (line 7). Which of these words is a determiner?
    Tick the box next to the correct answer.

    A   in   ☐

    B   these   ☐

    C   darkened   ☐

    D   depths   ☐

4. Explain how anglerfish are able to swallow prey twice their size.

    _____

    _____

TURN OVER ➡

5. How did the anglerfish get its name?

_____

_____

6. Give another word or phrase that means the same as "protruding" (line 11).

_____

7. Give one way that a vampire squid is like a vampire.

_____

_____

8. Explain in your own words why the Dumbo octopus is described as a "less monstrous sea creature" (line 17).

_____

_____

9. Which of the following statements is true?
   Tick the box next to the correct answer.

   A   The deep ocean is desolate.   ☐

   B   We have a profound understanding of the deep ocean.   ☐

   C   Technology is helping our understanding of the deep ocean.   ☐

   D   There are many plants and animals in the deep ocean.   ☐

END OF TEST

/ 9

Test 26: Proofreading

You have **10 minutes** to do this test. Work as quickly and accurately as you can.

> This passage contains some spelling mistakes.
> Write the passage out again with the correct spellings.

1. Joanna could never concentrate in phisics lessons. She sat daydreaming at her desk, when suddenally the teacher startled her with a loud clap. She abruptly became concious that the whole class had turned round to gork at her being scalded.

   _____

   _____

   _____

   _____

> This passage has some punctuation mistakes.
> Write the passage out again with the correct punctuation.

2. "Who would like a biscuit" shouted, callum. Unsurprisingly a wave of children descended upon him almost knocking him over.

   _____

   _____

   _____

TURN OVER ➡

For each numbered line, choose the word or phrase which completes the passage correctly. The passage needs to make sense and be written in correct English. Circle the correct letter.

3. Grizzly bears are one of the **large enlarge largest big largen** species of land
                                              A   **B**   **C**   **D**   **E**

4. carnivore on the planet, **or and in without if** those living on Kodiak Island
                                    A   **B**   **C**   **D**   **E**

5. off the coast of Alaska **rivals rivalling rivaled rival rivaling** even the size of
                                A   **B**   **C**   **D**   **E**

6. polar bears. Grizzly bears are omnivores **due to because despite accept when**
                                           A   **B**   **C**   **D**   **E**

7. their diet **part mostly most whole some** consists of berries and nuts as well
               A   **B**   **C**   **D**   **E**

8. as **for some an them a** larger animals such as moose and deer.
     A **B** **C** **D** **E**

9. **While However So Before During** the season when salmon migrate upstream,
   A   **B**   **C**   **D**   **E**

10. grizzly bears can be seen **standing stander stands stand standed** in the rivers
                               A   **B**   **C**   **D**   **E**

trying to catch them.

END OF TEST

/ 18

You have **10 minutes** to do this test. Work as quickly and accurately as you can.

Read this poem carefully and answer the questions that follow.

An abridged extract from The Fire Brigade

Hark! high over the rattle and clamour and clatter
Of traffic-filled streets, do you hear that loud noise?
And pushing and rushing to see what's the matter,
Like herds of wild cattle, go pell-mell* the boys.

5   There's a fire in the city! the engines are coming!
The bold bells are clanging, "Make way in the street!"
The wheels of the hose-cart are spinning and humming
In time to the music of galloping feet.

At windows and doorways crowd questioning faces;
10 There's something about it that quickens one's breath.
How proudly the brave fellows sit in their places —
And speed to the conflict that may be their death!

Still faster and faster and faster and faster
The grand horses thunder and leap on their way.
15 The red foe is yonder, and may prove the master;
Turn out there, bold traffic — turn out there, I say!

They speed like a comet — they pass in a minute;
The boys follow on like a tail to a kite;
The commonplace street has but traffic now in it —
20 The great fire engines have swept out of sight.

* pell-mell — *quickly and chaotically*

Ella Wheeler Wilcox

TURN OVER ➡

                Test 27

1.   What type of word is "over" (line 1)?

_____

2.   Find a phrase from the first verse that contains a simile.

_____

3.   Which of the following sounds are not described in the poem?
      Tick the box next to the correct answer.

   A   Bells pealing   ☐

   B   Horses neighing   ☐

   C   Wheels turning   ☐

   D   Traffic in the street   ☐

4.   "At windows and doorways crowd questioning faces" (line 9). What type of word
      is "crowd" as it is used in the text? Tick the box next to the correct answer.

   A   Noun   ☐

   B   Verb   ☐

   C   Adverb   ☐

   D   Adjective   ☐

5.   Find a phrase from the poem which suggests the crowd find the fire engine exciting.

_____

_____

6. "The red foe is yonder, and may prove the master" (line 15).
   Explain what this line means in your own words.

   _____

   _____

7. Which of the words below is closest in meaning to "bold" as it is used on line 16?
   Tick the box next to the correct answer.

   A   Furious   ☐

   B   Brazen   ☐

   C   Grand   ☐

   D   Busy   ☐

8. Which of these statements is false? Tick the box next to the correct answer.

   A   The firefighters look afraid.   ☐

   B   The fire engine is pulled by horses.   ☐

   C   Traffic in the street makes way for the fire engine.   ☐

   D   The fire engine passes by quickly.   ☐

9. "The boys follow on like a tail to a kite" (line 18).
   Explain what this line means in your own words.

   _____

   _____

END OF TEST

/ 9

Time for some puzzles. These two will test your **word-meaning** and **spelling** skills.

Common Ground

The word pairs below each have a word in common. Find the word that links them and fill in the gaps. The word in the middle should have a similar meaning to the word on the left **and** the word on the right.

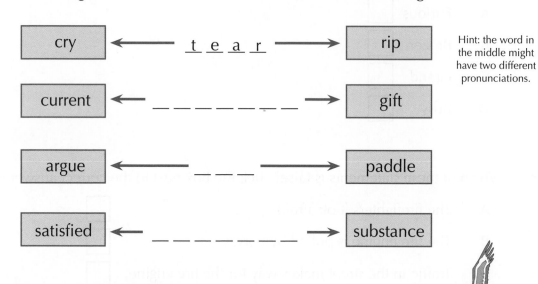

| cry | ← t e a r → | rip |

Hint: the word in the middle might have two different pronunciations.

| current | ← _ _ _ _ _ _ _ _ → | gift |

| argue | ← _ _ _ → | paddle |

| satisfied | ← _ _ _ _ _ _ _ _ → | substance |

Alphabet Anagram

The cloud contains all the letters of the alphabet, except six.

Work out which letters are missing and rearrange them to spell out a type of bird.

Missing letters:

m x s h u
t j v l
c f
d r w
a q
z b k y

The type of bird is a _ _ _ _ _ _ .

Test 28: Proofreading

You have **10 minutes** to do this test. Work as quickly and accurately as you can.

> For each numbered line, choose the word, or group of words, which completes the passage correctly. The passage needs to make sense and be written in correct English. Circle the correct letter.

1. **Accords**   **Accordingly**   **Accord**   **According**   **Accorded**   to legend, the griffin is the

  A   B   C   D   E

    king of all creatures. This mythical animal has an eagle's head, wings and

2. talons, **and**   **also**   **as**   **as well**   **onto**   the body of a lion. Due to the combined

 A   B   C   D   E

3. **strong**   **stronger**   **strongest**   **strength**   **strengthen**   and courage of these two

 A   B   C   D   E

4. creatures, the griffin **be**   **is**   **am**   **are**   **has**   seen as a symbol of power.

 A   B   C   D   E

> This passage contains some spelling mistakes.
> Write the passage out again with the correct spellings.

5. We are delighted to anounce that there are still plenty of tickits available for tomorrow's performance. It's guaranted to be a wonderfull evening of music and commedy.

_____

_____

_____

TURN OVER

              Test 28

This passage contains some punctuation mistakes. Each numbered line has either one mistake or no mistake. For each line, work out which group of words contains a mistake, and circle the correct letter. Circle N if there is no mistake.

6. The realisation hit me as I took my first step down the driveway. my stomach

          A   B   C   D   N

7. dropped as I spun around, desperately hoping there was still time, but it

          A   B   C   D   N

8. was too late Hannah had already pulled the front door closed and it slammed

          A   B   C   D   N

9. shut before my eyes. She looked confused as I let out a groan of frustration. I've

          A   B   C   D   N

10. forgotten my keys!" I cried miserably pushing the door and trying the handle

          A   B   C   D   N

11. even though I knew it wouldnt achieve anything. I peered through the living

          A   B   C   D   N

12. room window and on the other side of the glass I saw my keys lying uselessly, on

          A   B   C   D   N

13. the coffee table. "I'll call Nadia" Hannah said with a sigh. "She has a spare set."

          A   B   C   D   N

END OF TEST

/ 18

Test 29: Proofreading

You have **10 minutes** to do this test. Work as quickly and accurately as you can.

> For each numbered line, choose the word, or group of words,
> which completes the passage correctly. The passage needs to make
> sense and be written in correct English. Circle the correct letter.

1. It **have   will   must   is   had** been raining all day, which was especially annoying
    A   B   C   D   E

2. because Mr Dow had promised that the class **can   could   couldn't   must   ought**
                                                  A   B   C   D   E

3. play rounders after lunch. Gavin sighed, **stare   stares   stared   is staring   staring**
                                                 A   B   C   D   E

4. out of the window. He would just have to **hopes   hoped   hope   hoping   hopeful**
                                                 A   B   C   D   E

    that the weather cleared up by lunchtime.

> This passage has some punctuation mistakes.
> Write the passage out again with the correct punctuation.

5. louise was hosting a party and she was almost ready to welcome, her first guests
    She had tidied the house put out some snacks and blown up the Balloons

    _____

    _____

    _____

TURN OVER ➡

81

This passage contains some spelling mistakes. Each numbered line has either one mistake or no mistake. For each line, work out which group of words contains a mistake, and circle the correct letter. Circle N if there is no mistake.

6. After four years at the school, Aaron was surprised to reallise he was actually sad

    A   **B**   **C**   **D**   **N**

7. to leave. He'd always been eager to escape when the bell rang, signelling the end

    A   **B**   **C**   **D**   **N**

8. of lessons. He was typically the first one out of the building, sprynting out

    A   **B**   **C**   **D**   **N**

9. of the gate and across the feild, but it was strange to know that this would be the

    A   **B**   **C**   **D**   **N**

10. last time he'd take this route home. He'd made plenty of memeries at school,

    A   **B**   **C**   **D**   **N**

11. from hilarious ones to embarrasing ones, and found some brilliant friends too.

    A   **B**   **C**   **D**   **N**

12. At least he would never have to endure another one of Mr Kenway's dreary maths

    A   **B**   **C**   **D**   **N**

13. lessons or eat another serveing of the soggy mess they claimed was shepherd's pie.

    A   **B**   **C**   **D**   **N**

END OF TEST

/ 18

You have **10 minutes** to do this test. Work as quickly and accurately as you can.

Read this passage carefully and answer the questions that follow.

Vatican City

The smallest country in the world has less than six hundred citizens, around one thousand residents and an area of only 0.44 km². It also boasts a unique location. The State of Vatican City is a country within a country — it exists entirely inside Italy's capital city of Rome. Tourists flock in their millions to visit sites such as
5 St Peter's Basilica and the Sistine Chapel, which feature some of the world's most famous sculptures and paintings.

When they cross the border from Italy into Vatican City, visitors don't need to worry about using a different currency, swapping out their Italian phrasebooks or going through passport control. Nevertheless, the small area within Rome is a
10 country in its own right. The country is ruled by the Pope, the head of the Catholic Church. Most citizens of the country are clergy* or people working for the Pope in some other capacity, such as serving in the Pontifical Swiss Guard*.

While present-day Italy is a single country, for centuries the area was made up of a number of individual states, each led by separate rulers. Some of these, the Papal
15 States, were ruled by the Pope. However, in the nineteenth century, the individual states merged to form one country. The Pope opposed this unification, but the Papal States were conquered and absorbed into the unified Kingdom of Italy. In 1929, after much dispute, the Lateran Treaty was signed — this established Vatican City as an independent state.

20 Since then, Vatican City has operated separately from the rule of Italy. For example, it remained neutral during the Second World War, while Italy did not. Although Rome was occupied by German troops in 1943, and later by Allied troops in 1944, Vatican City remained untouched and was respected as neutral territory.

* clergy — *the leaders of a religious group*
* Pontifical Swiss Guard — *soldiers responsible for the safety of the Pope*

TURN OVER ➡

1. What is unusual about Vatican City's location?

   _____

2. Which of the following statements about Vatican City is false?
   Tick the box next to the correct answer.

   A   You need your passport to enter the Vatican City. ☐

   B   It contains many renowned works of art. ☐

   C   It is a popular tourist attraction. ☐

   D   Italy and Vatican City share the same currency. ☐

3. According to the text, how was Italy different before the nineteenth century?
   Tick the box next to the correct answer.

   A   It was called 'the Papal States'. ☐

   B   It was made up of different independent states. ☐

   C   It was occupied by German troops. ☐

   D   Vatican City was the capital city. ☐

4. Which of the words below is closest in meaning to "merged" (line 16)?
   Tick the box next to the correct answer.

   A   Combined ☐

   B   Agreed ☐

   C   Fought ☐

   D   Collapsed ☐

5. Describe how the Pope felt about Italian unification.

    _____

6. According to the text, which of the following statements best describes
    what happened in 1929? Tick the box next to the correct answer.

    A   The Lateran Treaty was signed after peaceful discussion.   ☐

    B   The Pope conquered the Papal States.   ☐

    C   The Pope became the ruler of the Kingdom of Italy.   ☐

    D   Vatican City was declared separate from the rest of Italy.   ☐

7. Give another word or phrase that means the same as
    "operated" (line 20) as it is used in the text.

    _____

8. "Although Rome was occupied by German troops" (line 22).
    Which of these words is a conjunction?

    _____

9. "Vatican City remained untouched and was respected as neutral territory" (line 23).
    Explain what this means in your own words.

    _____

    _____

END OF TEST

/ 9

Phew! Take a break and practise your **word type** and **spelling** skills with these puzzles.

Present Predicament

Carrie has bought some presents for her friends, but she's forgotten to write their names on the labels. Work out which present belongs to which friend and write a name on each label.

The present with the **common noun** written on it is for Alena.

The present with the **collective noun** written on it is for Zach.

The present with the **abstract noun** written on it is for Lin.

The present with the **pronoun** written on it is for Kyle.

The present with the **proper noun** written on it is for Jules.

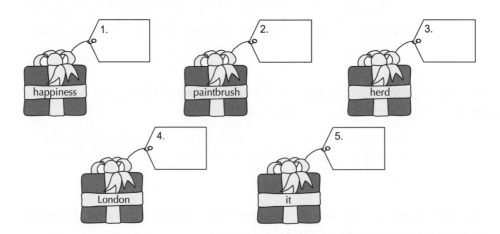

Keep Quiet

Leonard the librarian is organising some books, but he's realised that some of the titles are spelt incorrectly. Add the missing silent letter and write the correct spelling on the line.

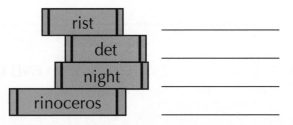

You have **10 minutes** to do this test. Work as quickly and accurately as you can.

> This passage contains some spelling mistakes.
> Write the passage out again with the correct spellings.

1. Waiting patiantly in the cue for the checkout, I realised that the person in front
    of me was Adam, an old acquaintance from school. I tapped him on the sholder
    — he turned around in confusion, but imediately recogised me.

    _____

    _____

    _____

    _____

> This passage has some punctuation mistakes.
> Write the passage out again with the correct punctuation.

2. Death Valley is a desert valley, in california, USA It's one of the hottest places on the
    planet holding the record for the highest air temperature recorded on Earth 56.7 °C)
    in 1913.

    _____

    _____

    _____

TURN OVER

For each numbered line, choose the word which completes the passage correctly. The passage needs to make sense and be written in correct English. Circle the correct letter.

3. Welsh cakes **is   are   would   was   am**   a traditional delicacy from Wales.
                   A **B**   **C**   **D**   **E**

4. A cross between a scone **with   from   and   of   by**   a pancake, these sweet
                          A   **B**   **C**   **D** **E**

5. treats are **make   makes   making   made   maker**   from simple pantry ingredients
            A   **B**   **C**   **D**   **E**

6. **such   so   also   including   since**   as flour, sugar, eggs and butter. Traditionally,
  A **B** **C**   **D**   **E**

7. **those   they   it   that   them**   were cooked on a hot bakestone, although these days
  A   **B**   **C** **D**   **E**

8. a griddle pan is more **common   commonly   commoner   commons   commonest**
                        A   **B**   **C**   **D**   **E**

9. used. Wales is **knowing   knows   known   knowed   know**   for its mining history
                 A   **B**   **C**   **D**   **E**

and these cakes are often called 'Welsh Miner Cakes' because they're small but filling

10. and would have been **easily   easy   ease   eases   easing**   to eat down the mines.
                  A   **B**   **C**   **D**   **E**

END OF TEST

/ 18

You have **10 minutes** to do this test. Work as quickly and accurately as you can.

Read this passage carefully and answer the questions that follow.

Buried Treasure

    Erin knew this forest better than anyone. She had spent years exploring its winding paths and climbing its gnarled trees, and now her feet moved instinctively along the muddy track. She felt certain that they were drawing closer and she picked up the pace. She could hear Ricky a few steps behind her, crashing through
5   the undergrowth, and she gave him a shout of encouragement. As they raced towards the clearing, her mind whirred with anticipation, her heart pounding. She skidded to a halt, breathless. This was it.

    Ricky came to an abrupt halt beside her. "It's definitely here?" he panted. "You're sure?"

10 "Yes. I remember this place." She knelt at the base of the old oak tree, her hands scrabbling in the soft earth. By the time she had finished, there was dirt caked under her fingernails and mud splattered across her clothes. "Aha!" she cried, as her fingers brushed something solid beneath the surface.

    Triumphantly, she pulled the box from its hiding place, shaking off some of the
15 dirt. Looking at it now, it was an unassuming object. It was perfectly square, fitting easily into the palm of her hand. It was made from a dark wood that perhaps had once been smart and polished, gleaming like the surface of a mirror, but now it was dull and shabby. Ricky was already clutching the key in his hands. He was shaking too much and impatiently she took the key from him, wiping some of the mud onto
20 her trousers. She forced the key into the lock and it turned with a click.

    They looked at each other. Ricky nodded, grinning nervously. Erin took a deep breath and lifted the lid. The box was empty.

TURN OVER ➡

Test 32

Answer these questions about the text. You can refer back to the text if you need to.

1. Why can Erin make her way through the forest "instinctively" (line 2)?

_____

_____

2. "she picked up the pace" (lines 3-4). Explain what this means in your own words.

_____

3. Which of these statements is false? Tick the box next to the correct answer.

    A   Erin leads the way through the forest. ☐

    B   Erin and Ricky are both out of breath. ☐

    C   Ricky moves quietly through the forest. ☐

    D   Erin stops suddenly in the clearing. ☐

4. How does Erin know where the treasure is buried?
Tick the box next to the correct answer.

    A   She has been there before. ☐

    B   She is following a map. ☐

    C   Ricky showed her where to go. ☐

    D   She finds the place by chance. ☐

5. Write down a word from the text that means 'victoriously'.

_____

6. Which of the following statements best describes the box?
   Tick the box next to the correct answer.

   A The box is impressive to look at. ☐

   B The box is larger than Erin expected. ☐

   C The box has a polished surface. ☐

   D The box is old and scruffy. ☐

7. "like the surface of a mirror" (line 17). What is this phrase an example of?
   Tick the box next to the correct answer.

   A Personification ☐

   B A simile ☐

   C Onomatopoeia ☐

   D A metaphor ☐

8. Why does Erin open the box instead of Ricky?

_____

9. "Erin took a deep breath and lifted the lid" (lines 21-22).
   Which of these words is an adjective?

_____

END OF TEST

/ 9

Test 33: Comprehension

You have **10 minutes** to do this test. Work as quickly and accurately as you can.

Read this passage carefully and answer the questions that follow.

Pluto

Pluto was originally regarded as the ninth planet from the Sun in the Solar System. However, after much controversy, Pluto was later demoted and reclassified as a dwarf planet. It was discovered in 1930 by Clyde Tombaugh, who was working from the Lowell Observatory in Arizona, USA. The public's enthusiastic response to the
5   news led to a flood of suggestions about what this new discovery should be called. The name 'Pluto', after the god of the underworld in classical mythology, was proposed by an English schoolgirl.

Pluto is much smaller than the Earth, about one-sixth the mass of our Moon, and is made up of ice and rock. It has five known moons — most take their names
10   from the aspects of Greek mythology associated with the underworld, such as Styx (the name of the river that flows between the worlds of the living and the dead) and Charon (the boatman who ferries dead souls across the river).

The debate over Pluto's status as a planet flared up in the 1990s when further research and exploration into the region surrounding Pluto (the Kuiper belt) was
15   performed. A number of other objects were discovered in the region, some of them almost the same size as Pluto. This cast doubt over Pluto's status — why should it be called a planet if these other objects weren't?

At the time, there was no official definition for the term 'planet'. However, when the International Astronomical Union issued three criteria for what constituted a
20   planet in 2006, Pluto's fate was sealed. Pluto fulfilled two of the criteria but failed to meet the third, therefore it could no longer be considered a planet. A planet or not, Pluto remains an object of fascination, and hopefully one day scientists will uncover the mysteries of this distant dwarf planet.

92

Answer these questions about the text. You can refer back to the text if you need to.

1. According to the text, which of the following statements must be true?
   Tick the box next to the correct answer.

   A   Everyone agreed that Pluto should be called a dwarf planet. ☐

   B   There are eight planets in between Pluto and the Sun. ☐

   C   Pluto has always been regarded as a dwarf planet. ☐

   D   Pluto was discovered in the early 19th century. ☐

2. How did people react to Pluto's discovery?

   _____

3. Which of the following statements about "Styx" (line 10) is true?
   Tick the box next to the correct answer.

   A   It's the name of the ferryman in Greek mythology. ☐

   B   It's the name of the underworld in Greek mythology. ☐

   C   It's the name of a dwarf planet. ☐

   D   It's the name of one of Pluto's moons. ☐

4. "further research and exploration into the region" (lines 13-14).
   Which of these words is a preposition?

   _____

TURN OVER ➡

93

5. According to the text, what first caused scientists to question Pluto's planet status?

_____

_____

6. Write down a word or phrase from the text that means 'formal'.

_____

7. What happened in 2006 that meant Pluto was no longer considered a planet?
   Tick the box next to the correct answer.

   A   The International Astronomical Union was founded.   ☐

   B   Large objects were discovered in the Kuiper belt.   ☐

   C   New conditions were introduced for defining a planet.   ☐

   D   More was learnt about the region surrounding Pluto.   ☐

8. Which of these words is closest in meaning to "fate" (line 20)
   as it is used in the text? Tick the box next to the correct answer.

   A   Failure   ☐

   B   Destiny   ☐

   C   Disgrace   ☐

   D   Situation   ☐

9. "uncover the mysteries of this distant dwarf planet" (lines 22-23).
   Explain what this means in your own words.

_____

END OF TEST

/ 9